GET SMART
MATH

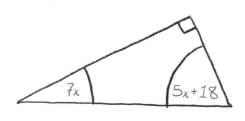

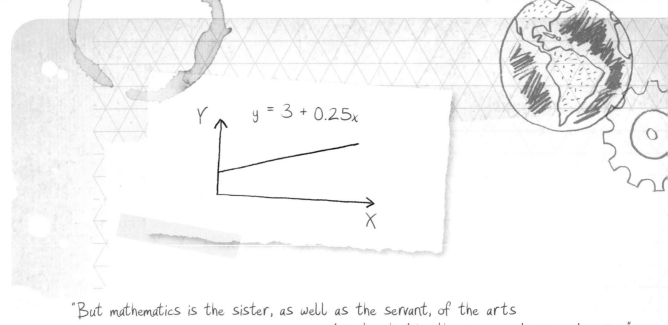

$$y = 3 + 0.25x$$

"But mathematics is the sister, as well as the servant, of the arts
and is touched by the same madness and genius."

[Marston Morse]

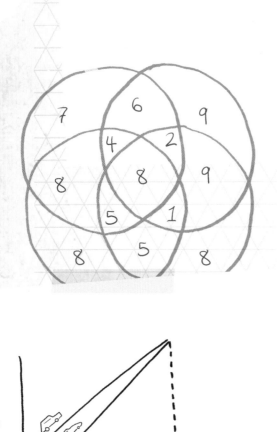

doodle something creative here

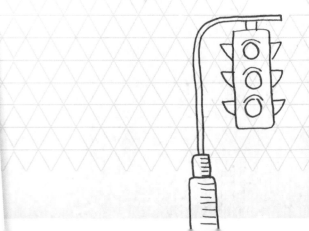

GIFT RECEIPT

Barnes & Noble Booksellers #2893
235 Union Street
Waterbury, CT 06706
203-759-7125

STR:2893 REG:006 TRN:6765 CSHR:Jada R

Get Smart Math   T1
    9780957423244   B.HL G
    (1 @ B.HL)

Connect with us on Social Media!

Facebook: @bnwaterbury
Twitter: @bnwaterbury
Instagram: bnwaterbury

048.02C   12/02/2018 02:28PM

CUSTOMER COPY

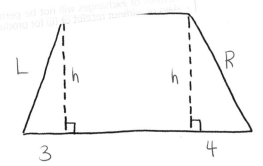

$$x = \frac{-b \pm \sqrt{b^2 - 4ac}}{2a}$$

PAPERWASP

NOT SMART, BE SMART, GET SMART!

Get Smart - Math ...is a truly stimulating numbers explosion for all the family. It will flick the math switch for even the most academic minds to show off their calculating skills.

> A **mathematical theory** is not to be considered **complete** until you have made it **so clear** that you can **explain it** to the **first man** whom **you meet** on the street.
>
> [David Hilbert]

This series is destined to be a classic when it comes to number crunching fun, so here's how it works...

There are over 100 questions to solve with one question per page and oodles of doodle space for your answers of course!

Try doodling here - it's your workbook after all - the idea is to be creative, so don't be afraid to show what you're thinking by scribbling your workings here

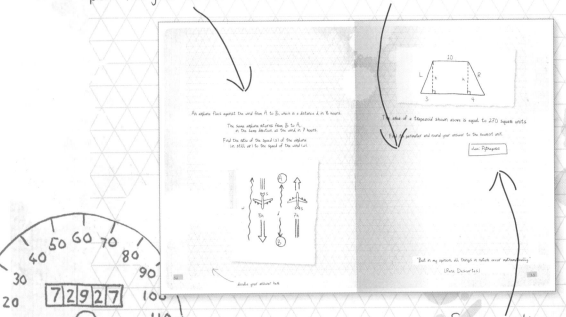

Some questions even have a clue - it might just save some brain ache!

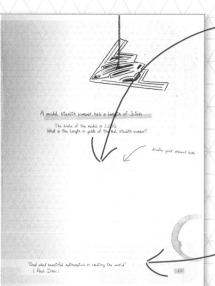

Getting stuck? Then doodle something here. Masterpiece or scribble, Nobel-prize worthy or really inane, it all counts.

Look - loads of space for more of your visual workings, so really get stuck in!

Just look at these fascinating quotes from famous Mathematicians and Physicists - you'll see them dotted around the pages for real inspiration.

Some questions are trickier than others, but we haven't left you completely stumped - the answers are at the back of the book for those who really can't get it!

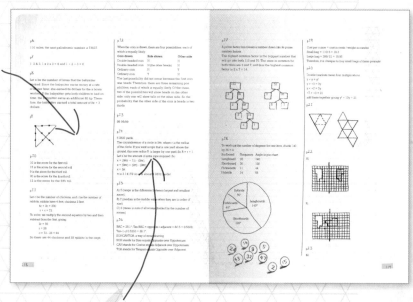

How boring! We've even shown you how to solve the questions

What are you waiting for? GET SMART now...
after all Einstein had to practice!

A car odometer reading shows 72927 miles.

This is a palindromic number.

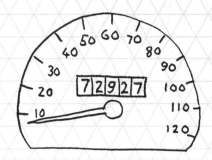

What is the minimum number of miles you would need to travel to see another palindromic number on this car's odometer?

Find three whole, positive numbers
that have the same answer

when multiplied together as when added together.

"Pure mathematics is, in its way, the poetry of logical ideas".
[Albert Einstein]

A babysitter earns $8 an hour for babysitting
two children and an additional $3 tip when
both children are put to bed on time.

If the babysitter gets the children to bed on time, what expression
could be used to determine how much the babysitter earned?

Ⓐ 8x + 3, where x is the number of hours
Ⓑ 3x + 8, where x is the number of hours
Ⓒ x(8 + 2) + 3, where x is the number of children

doodle your answer here

Nine dots are arranged in a three by three square.

Connect each of the nine dots
using only four straight
lines and without lifting your pen from the paper.

A solo dice game is played where, on each turn,
a normal pair of dice is rolled.

. The score is calculated by taking the product, rather than the sum,
of the two numbers shown on the dice.

On a particular game, the score for the second roll is five
more than the score for the first; the score for the third roll
is six less than that of the second; the score for the fourth
roll is eleven more than that of the third; and the score for the
fifth roll is eight less than that of the fourth.

What was the score for each of these five throws?

There are several chickens and rabbits in a cage (and no other types of animals).

There are 72 heads and 200 feet inside the cage. How many chickens are there, and how many rabbits?

A box contains two quarters.

One is a double-headed coin, and the other is an ordinary coin, heads on one side, and tails on the other.

You draw one of the coins from a box
    and look at one of the sides.
        Assuming it is heads, what is the probability
    that the other side shows heads also?

"Mathematics is as much an aspect of culture as it is a collection of algorithms."
    [Carl Boyer]

doodle your answer here

How can you express the number 100 using just six nines (no other digits)
and one of the following mathematical symbols: +, =, -, /, x?

An artist plans to tie a rope made from fishing lines found on beaches around the earth's equator to highlight marine pollution.

Then he decides it will be seen better if it is held up one yard high on sticks. How much more rope does he need?

Assume the earth is perfectly spherical.

clue: the answer is related to π

Seven students took a Math and English test
with the following scores out of ten.

name	math	english
Pete	7	7
Nancy	8	5
Drew	8	6
Paul	6	8
Antonio	5	6
Helen	6	7
Mina	8	3

What were the:

Ⓐ Range of English scores

Ⓑ Median score for Math

Ⓒ Mean score for English?

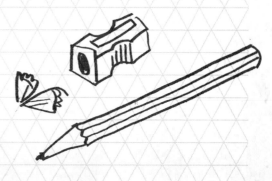

ABC is a right-sided triangle
with the following measurements

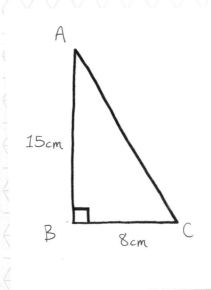

Work out the angle BAC using what you
know about the relationship between opposite
and adjacent lengths.

clue: SOHCAHTOA

Draw a prime number tree for 112 and 70.

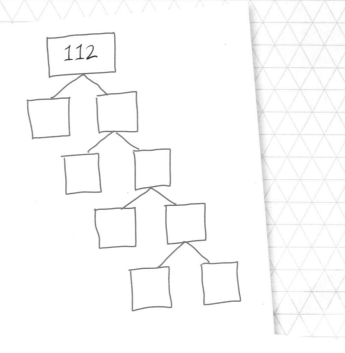

What is the highest common factor?

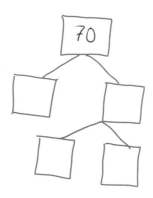

doodle your answer here

Laura audited the range of surfboards she had
in her storeroom and hoped to present it as a

pie chart to help her visualize the information.

Complete the table below
and draw the pie chart using its contents:

surfboard	frequency	angle in pie chart
longboard	35	140
shortboard	30	?
fishboard	?	44
hybrid	14	?

Peanuts come in small bags and large bags.

A small bag of 6 oz costs $1.10 and a large bag of 21 oz costs $3.98.

Which bag is better value for money?

Expand and simplify $(y + 7)(y + 3)$

doodle your answer here

Sketch the nets of a tetrahedron
(triangular-based pyramid) and an octahedron.

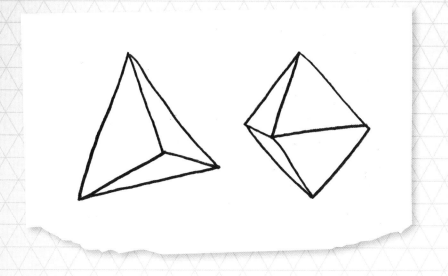

"But mathematics is the sister, as well as the servant, of the arts
and is touched by the same madness and genius."

[Marston Morse]

Draw the reflection

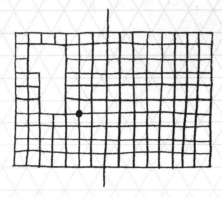

(A) Draw the reflection of the shape in the line shown.

(B) Draw a 90° clockwise rotation of the shape using the black circle as the center.

The recommended retail price of a Dashcam is $90.

Electronics-to-Go is selling the device
with 20% off the recommended price.

Eyes-on-the-Road is selling the device
with a discount of 2/9 off the recommended price...

What is the difference in price between

Electronics-to-Go and Eyes-on-the-Road?

Drawing an equation

(A) Complete the table for the equation $y = 3x + 1$:

x	-3	-2	-1	0	1	2	3	4
y								

(B) Draw the graph of $y = 3x + 1$:

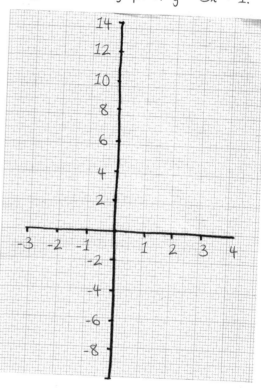

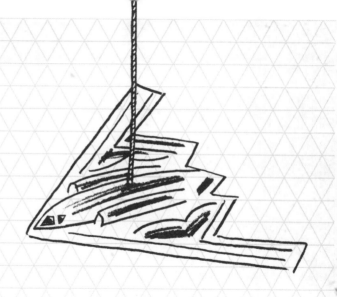

A model stealth bomber has a length of 3.5in

The scale of the model is 1:250.
What is the length in yards of the real stealth bomber?

doodle your answer here

"God used beautiful mathematics in creating the world."
[Paul Dirac]

A breakfast cereal box has longest sides measuring two units more than the shortest sides, and middle length sides one unit longer than the shortest side.

The total surface area of the cuboid is 52 units².

(A) Construct an equation to calculate the surface area of the box.

(B) Use the equation to calculate the length of the shortest side.

ABC is a straight line. BCD is a triangle.

ABDE is a quadrilateral.

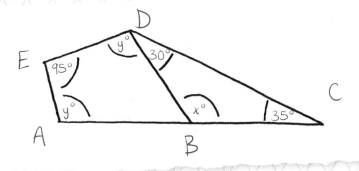

A) Work out the value of x.   B) Work out the value of y.

clue: internal angles

Danny goes to a hardware store
and buys 3 pounds of nails
He also buys 0.4 pounds of washers.

The total cost is $6.93.

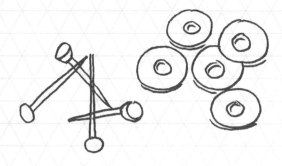

The nails were labeled at $1.95 per pound but there was
no price marked on the washers.

Work out the cost of 1 pound of washers.

"Mathematics compares the most diverse phenomena
and discovers the secret analogies that unite them."
[Joseph Fourier]

Sean and Michael are going to see a movie.

The probability that Sean will arrive late at the theater is 0.2
The probability that Michael will arrive late is 0.6

The two events are independent.

Ⓐ Complete the diagram;

Ⓑ What is the probability that Sean
    and Michael will both arrive late?

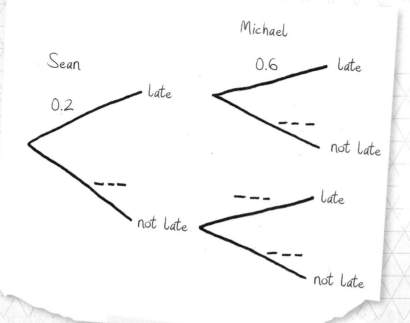

Marie has an unusual shaped water tank
with a trapezium-shaped cross-section:

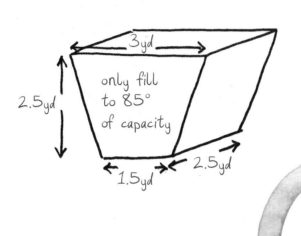

3yd

only fill
to 85°
of capacity

2.5yd

1.5yd   2.5yd

It is empty and needs filling up, so she turns on a hose and water flows into the tank.
After 1 minute there are 150 gallons in it.

Assuming the same flow rate, work out how many more
minutes Marie will need to fill the tank to 85% capacity.

Two triangles NOP and ABC are mathematically similar

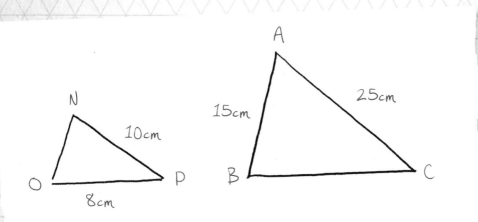

Angle N = angle A and angle P = angle C

not drawn to scale

Calculate the following lengths: (a) NO and (b) BC.

An airplane flies against the wind from A to B, which is a distance d, in 8 hours.

The same airplane returns from B to A,
in the same direction as the wind, in 7 hours.

Find the ratio of the speed (s) of the airplane
(in still air) to the speed of the wind (w).

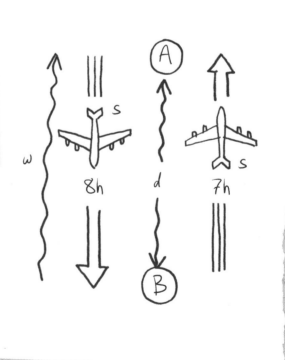

doodle your answer here

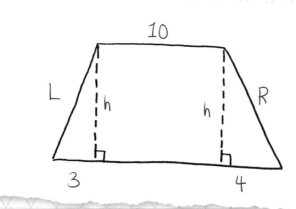

The area of a trapezoid shown above is equal to 270 square units

Find its perimeter and round your answer to the nearest unit.

clue: Pythagoras

"But in my opinion, all things in nature occur mathematically."

[René Descartes]

A real estate agent negotiated a 5% commission on the selling price of a house.

If his commission was $13,750,
what was the selling price of the house?

In a shop, the cost of 4 shirts, 4 pairs of trousers and 2 hats is $560.
The cost of 9 shirts, 9 pairs of trousers and 6 hats is $1,290.

What is the total cost of 1 shirt, 1 pair of trousers and 1 hat?

clue: simultaneous equations

doodle your answer here

Two candles are the same height.

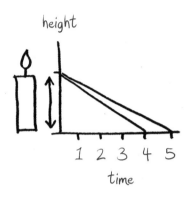

One burns down completely in 4 hours and
the other burns down completely in 5 hours.

After lighting at the same time, how long
before one is twice the height of the other?

"Mathematics is the language with which God wrote the universe."
    Galileo

A lottery prize of $2,000 is placed in a savings account
at 3% per annum compounded annually.

How much is in the account after one year, two years and three years?

Jack sets off from his office to the Hamptons for a weekend
party at 50 miles per hour (mph) in his car.

Patricia sets off by car from the same office 30 minutes later.

What speed will Patricia choose to arrive at the same time as Jack,
given that she expects the trip to take 2 hours?

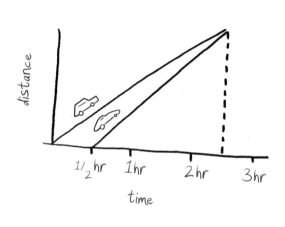

clue: speed = distance/time

A fan blade spins at 3,000 revolutions per minute.

How many degrees does it rotate in one second?

Pedro the cheesemonger is cutting wedges for sale from a whole brie cheese.

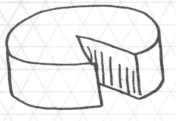

Each wedge must have a 35-degree angle and the whole cheese weighs 900g.

What weight of cheese will Pedro have left over after cutting as many wedges as possible?

doodle your answer here

Stripes on the American flag

The American flag has 13 equally spaced, horizontal red and white stripes, with an inset blue rectangle bearing 50 stars.

What part of the flag is white stripes?

40%

100%

A globe representing the Earth is depicted
with 17 parallels and 12 meridians.

How many areas do these lines divide the surface of the globe into?

The results from a survey of 80 clients using four different Internet service providers (ISPs) can be represented as a Venn diagram.

It shows how 8 clients used all four ISPs.

If the proportions shown are the same in a region of 10,000 clients, how many are expected to use at least 2 ISPs?

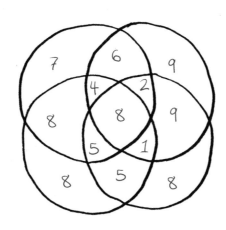

There are 8 sets of traffic lights

Each set with three different colored lights, at a major border crossing.

How many ways can the lights be put on such
that no neighboring lights have the same color?

A grocer weighed three pomegranates in pairs and the weights of these pairs were 400, 424 and 448 g.

What is the weight of the lightest pomegranate?

doodle your answer here

A cruise ship leaves port on a bearing of 28° and after traveling 7.5 miles is instructed to turn due east and travel for a further 4.1 miles to reach a small island where there is a beach party.

How far is the island from the port and what is its bearing?

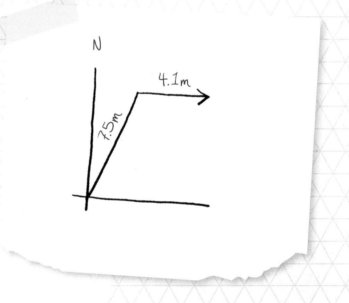

clue: think adjacent and supplementary to get started

A drawer contains 7 white and 5 black socks.

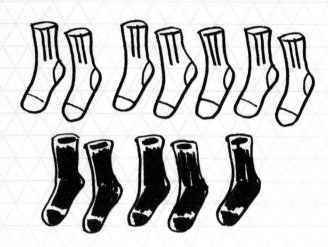

Lance takes out two socks at random.

Work out the probability that he takes a matching pair of socks of the same color.

"Mathematics is an art of human understanding.."
[William Thurston]

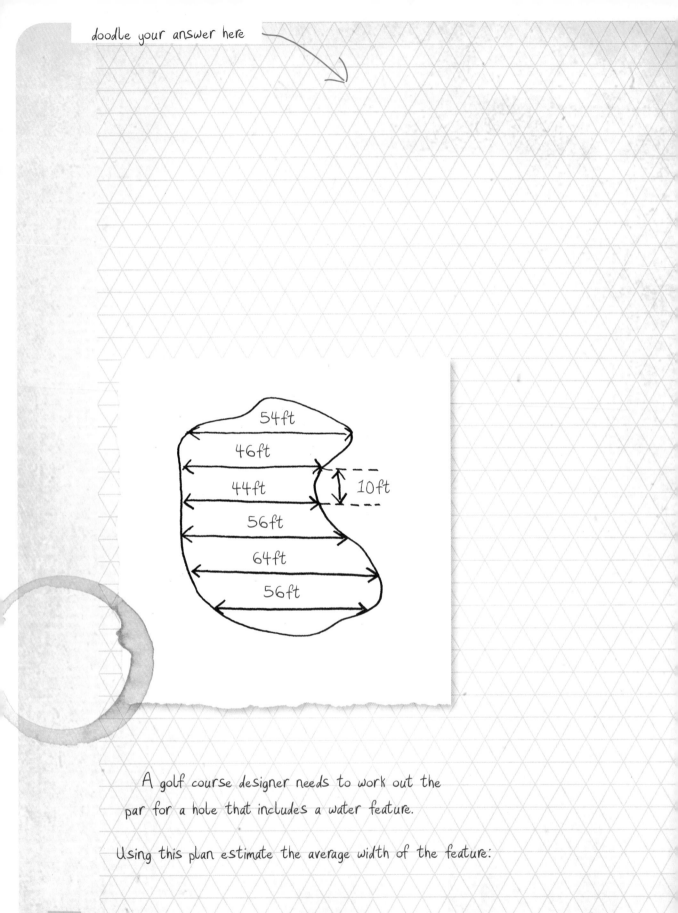

A golf course designer needs to work out the par for a hole that includes a water feature.

Using this plan estimate the average width of the feature:

A woman drinks 30 wheatgrass shots in 30 days.

Together with her daughter, they drink the same amount in 18 days.

How many days would it take for the daughter to drink this amount by herself?

X + Y = 678, where X and Y represent different whole numbers, and Y is 56 more than X.

Calculate the values of X and Y.

A yellow cab charges a fixed fee of $2.25,
plus 75 cents for each mile of a journey before 9pm.
The fixed fee increases to $4.00 after this time.

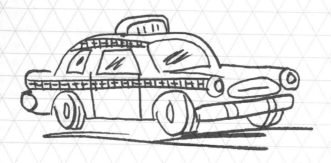

A passenger wants to travel 7 miles to a concert at 7pm
and then be brought home again at 11pm.

How much will the overall journey cost?

A man in a fishing competition catches his first fish after 30 minutes, then each next fish 2 minutes faster than the previous one.

How long will it take to catch 14 fish?

Circle the three numbers that have the same numerical value

99×10^6

0.99×10^8

9.9×10^9

99×10^6

$990,000 \times 10^2$

$99 \times 103 \times 10^5$

doodle your answer here

An elephant weighs 12,000lb and consumes 40,000 calories per day.

A mouse weighs 2oz and consumes 4 calories per day.
Which consumes more calories per ounce per day?

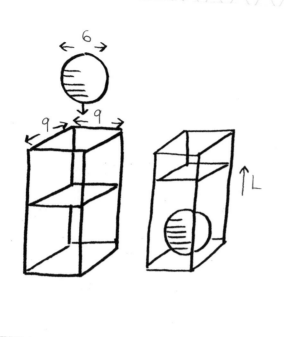

A concrete ball with diameter of 6 inches is dropped into a cuboid
    container with equal sides 9 inches wide and part filled with water.

    Calculate the increase in height of water in the container
assuming no splashing of water out of it (give answer in terms of π)

clue: volume of a sphere = $4/3\pi r^3$

"Mathematics is like checkers in being suitable for the young, not too difficult,
amusing, and without peril to the state."

[Plato]

10   12   19   22   24

53   32   41   45   49

Choose two digit numbers from the selection below
that add up to exactly 100.

Don't use any number more than once. How many numbers do you use?

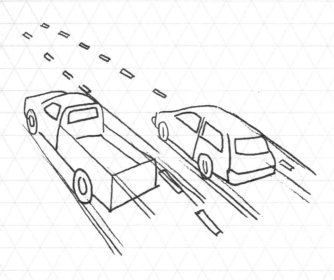

Alice starts driving on a motorway at 08:14 in the morning
to get to work just on time.

If she drives at a constant 48 mph, she gets to work 1 minute early,
but if traffic is a bit slower and she can drive at 45 mph,
she gets there 3 minutes late.

What time should she start work?

clue: Distance = Speed x Time.

What transformation of this triangle creates
an image with a vertex at the origin (0,0)?

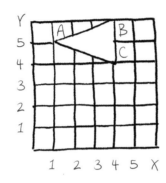

Four gears in a gear train have fixed centers.

The diameter of each gear is 7/8 of the gear to its left.
If the left-hand gear spins at 100 revolutions per minute (rpm),
how fast does the right-hand gear spin?

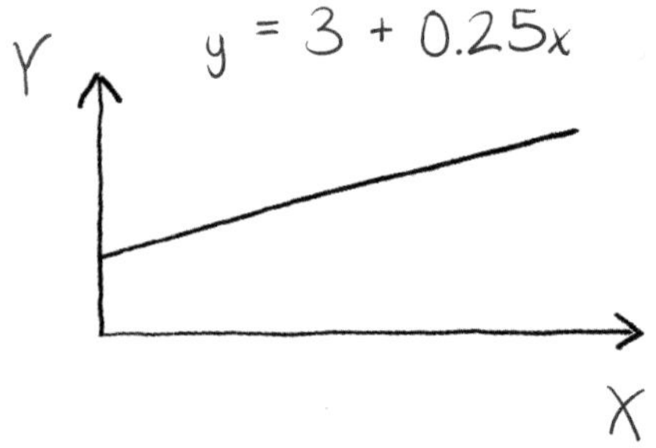

$$y = 3 + 0.25x$$

Which of the following points is not on the line?

A (1,2)
B (4,4)
C (8,5)
D (12,6)

Tim picked 100 zucchini from his yard between Monday and Friday.

Each day he picked six more zucchini than the previous day.

He used the zucchini to make cakes each day and each cake contained two zucchini, grated. How many cakes did Tim make on Wednesday?

"Mathematics is the music of reason."
[James Joseph Sylvester]

An architect draws the apex of a house, where the internal angles A, C and E are all right angles (90°). What is the sum of angles B and D?

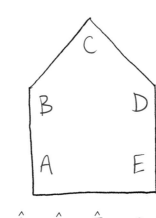

$$\hat{A} = \hat{C} = \hat{E} = 90°$$

$$\hat{B} + \hat{D} = ?$$

doodle your answer her

```
1    3    5

7    9    11

13   15   17

19   21...
```

What is the sum of the first 200 odd positive numbers?

When Big Island plays Little Island at soccer,
the odds are 5 to 3 that Big Island wins.

What is the probability that Big Island wins four games in a row?

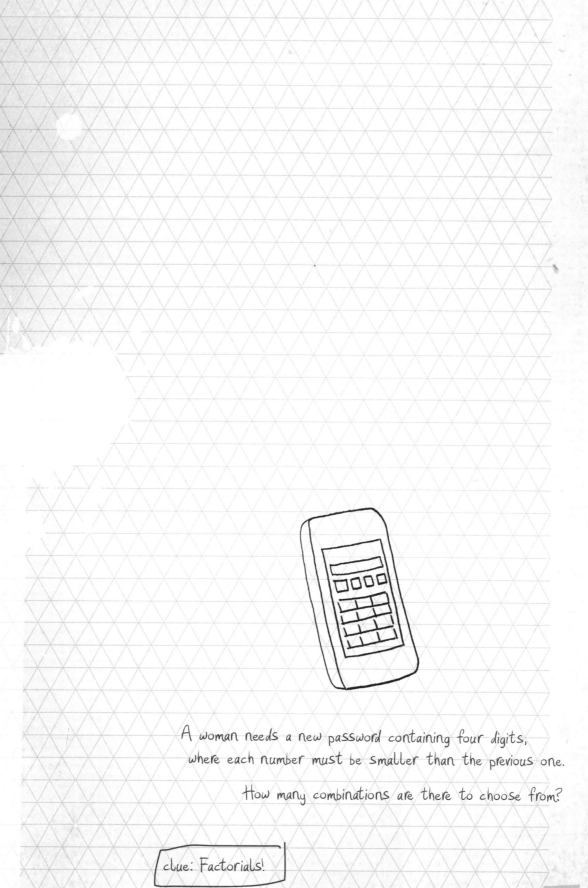

A woman needs a new password containing four digits,
where each number must be smaller than the previous one.

How many combinations are there to choose from?

clue: Factorials!

A student earns 17% tips from
each table of the restaurant he works.

She needs to earn a minimum of $6
per table to earn enough to pay her rent.

What is the minimum order needed per table to achieve this?

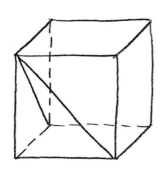

doodle your answer here

What is the longest number between 1 and 2,000
when depicted in Roman numerals?

I = 1 , II = 2, III = 3, IV = 4

V = 5, VI = 6, VII = 7 , VIII = 8

IX = 9, X = 10, L = 50, C = 100

D = 500, M = 1,000

Chinese calendar

This runs on a cycle of 12 years and each
year corresponds to one of 12 animals:

Rat, Ox, Tiger, Rabbit, Dragon, Snake, Horse,
Sheep, Monkey, Rooster, Dog and Pig.

The order of the sequence of animals never changes.

The year 2018 is year of the Dog. What animal will mark 2100?

Over a weekend, Chandler hikes 15 miles north from his home, then turns west and walks 8 miles, then turns south for 6 miles, before taking the shortest route home again.

How far did he hike in total?

clue: sketch the route

In a city, 75 per cent of the men are married to
80 per cent of the women.

Which is the correct ratio of men to women:

(A) 4:7

(B) 20:12

(C) 5:3

(D) 16/15

"Without mathematics, there's nothing you can do.
Everything around you is mathematics. Everything around you is numbers."
[Shakuntala Devi]

Jeff has two bags of sweets.

Bag 1 has 3 green and 5 red sweets.

Bag 2 has 1 green and 4 yellow sweets.

He takes one sweet at random from each bag.

What is the probability that he takes two green sweets?

doodle your answer here

Results of an election run by three
candidates are represented by a pie chart:

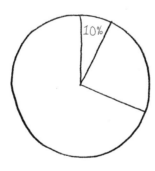

The losing candidate got 10% of the vote, while the
winner got three times as many votes as the runner up.
What percentage of votes did the winner receive?

Fifteen balls fit inside a billiard rack.

What is the largest number of balls that fit into the rack
when its side lengths are increased by 40 per cent?

"To solve math problems, you need to know the basic
mathematics before you can start applying it."
[Catherine Asaro]

Janice paid $27.68 for five mp3 downloads and two CDs.

If six mp3 downloads cost $15.36, how much does one CD cost?

The isosceles triangle XYZ has sides
of the lengths shown in the diagram:

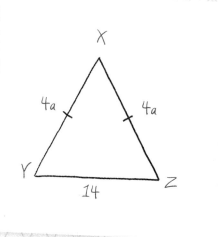

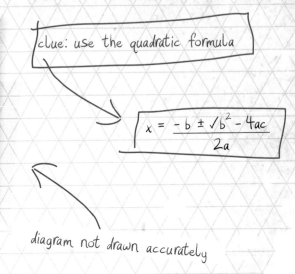

clue: use the quadratic formula

$$x = \frac{-b \pm \sqrt{b^2 - 4ac}}{2a}$$

diagram not drawn accurately

(A) What is the length of the perimeter of the triangle
in its simplest form in terms of p

(B) If the perimeter is p^2, calculate p correct to 1 decimal point.

The three numbers in each row and each column of a grid should add up to 259.

Which number in the grid is incorrect?

93	88	78
85	107	65
81	64	114

"Do not worry about your difficulties in Mathematics.
I can assure you mine are still greater."

[Albert Einstein]

In a survey, 7/8 of people asked if they trusted their president answered NO and the rest answered YES.

If 93 more people answered No than YES, how many people were in the survey?

The nth term of the sequence 0, 3, 8, 15... is $n^2 - 1$

What is the nth term for the following sequences:

(A) 1, 4, 9, 16...

(B) 4, 10, 20, 34...

(C) ½, 4, 13½, 32...

doodle your answer here

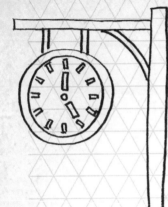

A station clock is 36 inches in diameter and its hands are showing exactly 5 o'clock.

(A) What is the area of the clock face between the minute and hour hand, in terms of π?

(B) What is the distance of the arc between the minute and hour hands, in terms of π?

The world population on July 1, 2018
was estimated at 7,632,819,325.

The growth rate for 2018 is 1.09% per year.

What is the expected population by the end of 2018?

Here is the tariff for a parking lot.

time	cost
Up to 1 hour	$1.20
Up to 2 hours	$2.00
Up to 3 hours	$3.00
Over 3 hours	$5.00

Car A parks at 08:45 and leaves at 11:44
Car B parks at 09:35 and leaves at 11:36

What is the parking charge for each car?

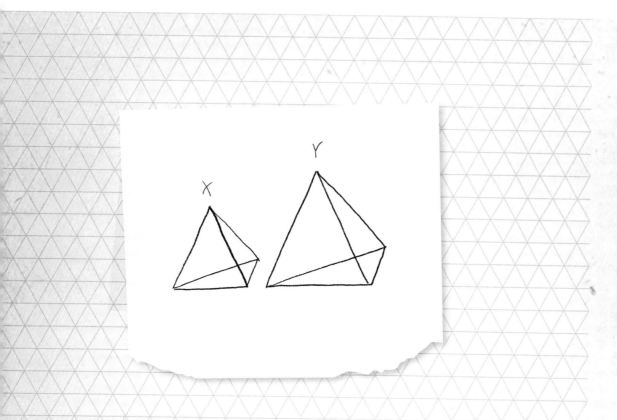

Two triangular based pyramids J and K are mathematically similar.

The surface area of J is 32 square inches and of K is 72 square inches. The volume of K is 540 cubic inches.

What is the volume of J ?

Aziz mixed up some mortar for laying bricks
using these proportions of dry materials:

> 1 part cement
> ¼ part lime
> 3½ parts sand

He made 20 pounds of mortar
of which 15% of the weight was water.

What were the weights of the dry materials?

doodle your answer here

Two Nascar racers drive circuits of a 2.5 mile speedway.

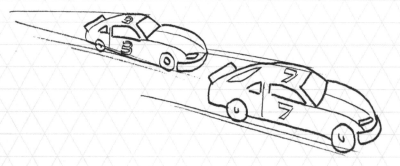

They start together but the faster Car A
completes their first circuit in 1 minute but Car B
completes their first circuit in 1 minute 20 seconds.

How many miles does each car need to travel before they pass
the start line at the same time?

A survey of 100 students showed how many hours they had spent revising for an important exam

time (t hours)	frequency
$0 \leqslant t < 4$	5
$4 \leqslant t < 8$	27
$8 \leqslant t < 12$	37
$12 \leqslant t < 16$	24
$16 \leqslant t < 20$	7

Draw a cumulative frequency graph and use this to estimate how many students revised for 13 or more hours.

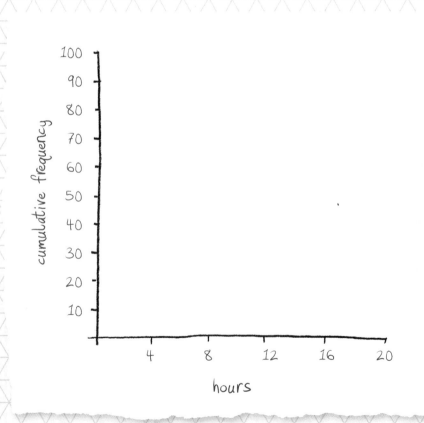

Dan, Beth, and Annette took a fun math test.

The total for the test was 75 marks.

They then told each other what they had got:

Dan got 57% of the 75 marks
Beth got 8/15 of the 75 marks
Annette got 43 of the 75 marks

Who got the highest mark?

"Mathematics knows no races or geographic boundaries;
for mathematics, the cultural world is one country."
[David Hilbert]

Work out the size of the smallest angle (in degrees) of the following right-angled triangle:

FLORIDA'S TURNPIKE

Redmond drives from his home near Miami
to a vacation house in Lake County.

He drives for 3 hours at 50mph
and then hits heavy traffic
on the Florida Turnpike slowing
his speed to 30mph for 150 miles.

Redmond said his average speed was 40 mph.
Is he correct?

doodle your answer here

Four different proportionality relationships between x and y are as follows:

Statement 1: y is directly proportional to x
Statement 2: y is inversely proportional to x
Statement 3: y is proportional to the square of x
Statement 4: y is inversely proportional to the square of x

The relationships are also shown as graphs.

Which graph represents which statement?

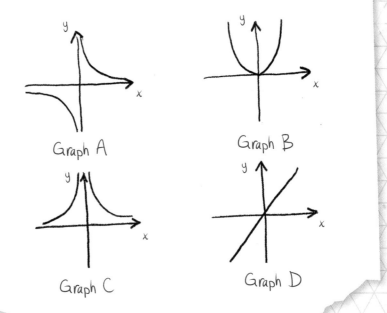

Graph A

Graph B

Graph C

Graph D

clue: think of each relationship as an
equation involving x, y, and the variable k.

"To me, mathematics, computer science, and the arts are insanely related. They're all creative expressions."
[Sebastian Thrun]

In the US, the average life expectancy is around 79 years.

The resting heart rate is on average 80 beats per minute.

On your 79th birthday, how many times will your heart have beaten?

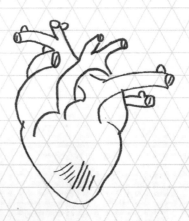

You have two pails.

One pail contains 5 gallons of water and the second 5 gallons of vinegar.

If you pour 1 gallon of water into the vinegar, and then return 1 gallon of this mixture to the water pail, what are the proportions of vinegar to water in the first pail?

Jamie has a piece of rope 16 feet long she lays out forming a square and then a rectangle 75% of the square's area.

What is the length of the rectangle if its width is half that of the square?

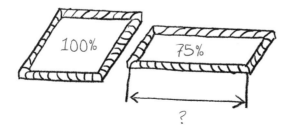

A circular lake has an area of 40 square miles.

Water taxis cost $4 per mile or per part of per mile.
What is the maximum amount that a taxi
could charge when crossing the lake once?

Perry sent an email to three work colleagues.

Everybody answered and copied their answers to all the others.
A total of 12 emails were sent.

How many emails would be sent if 400 people
communicated in the exact same way?

"While physics and mathematics may tell us how the universe began, they
are not much use in predicting human behavior because there are far too many
equations to solve. I'm no better than anyone else at understanding what
makes people tick, particularly women."

[Stephen Hawking]

A vertical-sided aquarium has a surface area of 500 square inches with the water level 1 inch from the top.

Paula puts in a castle for her fish to swim in that has a volume of 400 cubic inches and wants to add several fish each with a volume of 15 cubic inches each.

How many fish can she add before the water overflows?

Charm beads are evenly spaced around a bangle and the 11th bead is directly opposite the 29th bead. How many charm beads are there all together?

doodle your answer here

A slice of watermelon weighs 5 pounds and 92% of its weight is water.

After lying in the sun, the water makes up 78% of its weight.

So, how much does the slice now weigh?

Work out the values of x and y in this parallelogram:

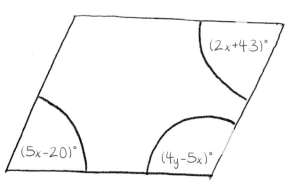

$(2x+43)°$

$(5x-20)°$

$(4y-5x)°$

clue: opposite angles in a parallelogram

A graph depicts a cyclist's journey:

(A) What is the acceleration between 5s and 8s?
(B) What is the acceleration between 8s and 10s?
(C) What is the total distance covered?

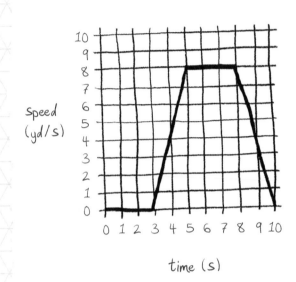

doodle your answer here

A carpenter cuts a piece of wood into five similar smaller pieces.

Each cut wastes 2.5% of the wood as sawdust.

What is the volume of each small piece as a percentage of the overall volume

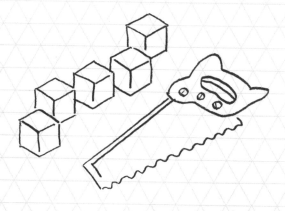

Matches are arranged in an anticlockwise spiral.

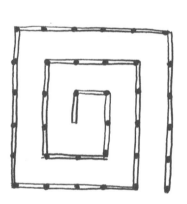

What is the minimum number of matches that
need to be moved to turn it into a clockwise spiral?

In an interview, a famous Hollywood actor says he is 44 years old if you do not count weekends and one winter month of each year when he is on holiday. How old is he really?

Thirty thousand shares in a windfarm start-up are sold to 150 buyers.
Each thousand shares are bought by either five men or four women.

How many male buyers buy the shares?

clue: male + female = 150

doodle your answer here

What is the missing number?

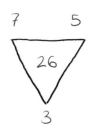 7 5 26 3

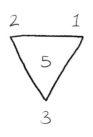 2 1 5 3

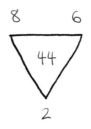 8 6 44 2

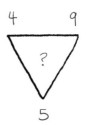 4 9 ? 5

"There should be no such thing as boring mathematics."
[Edsger Dijkstra]

Maria did a survey of 50 people's drinks preferences out of coffee, tea, and milk.

All 50 liked at least one of the three.
19 liked all three.
16 like tea and coffee but not milk
21 like coffee and milk
24 like tea and milk
40 like just coffee
1 likes just milk

A) What is the probability that a person chosen at random likes tea?

B) What is the probability that this tea drinker also likes one other drink?

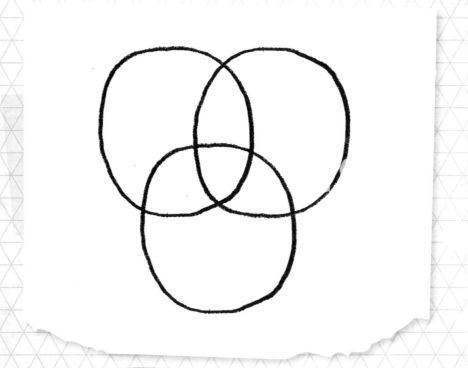

clue: Venn diagram

A watch loses 12 seconds in one hour
and was set right at 6 o'clock in the morning.

What time will it show at 3 o'clock
in the afternoon on the same day?

A farmer found that her orchard increased the number
of apples for picking by 100% each year.

In the sixth year the orchard produced 6,400 apples.
How many apples did it produce in the first year?

doodle your answer here

Twelve scouts go on an expedition.

They prepare enough food to last them 8 days.

Then just before they leave, a further 4 scouts join them but have brought no extra food.

How long will the food last the group?

"Obvious is the most dangerous word in mathematics."
[Eric Temple Bell]

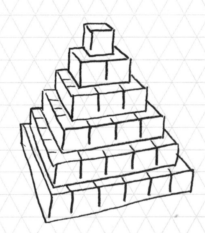

A model maker needs to paint a block pyramid with paint.

The coverage of paint is 1 gallon for 1 square surface of a block.

How much paint will the model maker need?

(NB bottom and internal surfaces will be left unpainted)

Rhianna went swimming yesterday.

Soon she realized she had covered one fifth of her intended distance.
After swimming six more lengths of the pool,
    she had covered one quarter of her intended distance.

How many lengths of the pool did she intend to complete?

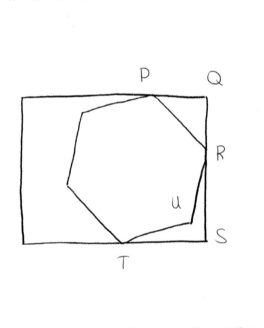

What is the sum of the angles QPR, QRP, SRU, and SUT in this diagram of a regular hexagon inside a rectangle?

clue: hexagon interior angles are 120°

Complete the missing values in the following grid

3		9		15
	8		14	
7		13		19
	12		18	
11		17		23

clue: Magic square!

doodle your answer here

Lenny earns 7.5% commission on every new professional camera that he sells.

In one week he received $280.50 commission.

What was his sales total?

The time lag between two generations in an average family is 25 years.

Given this, how many years ago did you have over 2,000 ancestors?

A cyclist has an average speed of 50 mph downhill and 20 mph uphill. .

She travels from one mountain viewpoint into a valley and up to another mountain viewpoint in 2 hours. The return trip takes 5 hours

How far is it between the viewpoints?

Which digit needs to be moved to make this sum correct?

43 − 56 = 8

doodle your answer here

p6

110 miles; the next palindromic number is 73037.

p7

1, 2 & 3; 1 x 2 x 3 = 6 and 1 + 2 + 3 = 6

p8

Let x be the number of hours that the babysitter worked. Since the babysitter earns money at a rate of $8 per hour, she earned 8x dollars for the x hours worked. If the babysitter gets both children to bed on time, the babysitter earns an additional $3 tip. Therefore, the babysitter earned a total amount of 8x + 3 dollars.

p9

p10

10 is the score for the first roll.

15 is the score for the second roll.

9 is the score for the third roll.

20 is the score for the fourth roll.

12 is the score for the fifth roll.

p11

Let c be the number of chickens, and r be the number of rabbits; rabbits have 4 feet, chickens 2 feet.

   4r + 2c = 200

   r + c = 72

To solve, we multiply the second equation by two and then subtract from the first, giving:

   2r = 56

   r = 28

   c = 72 - 28 = 44

So there are 44 chickens and 28 rabbits in the cage.

p12

When the coin is drawn, there are four possibilities, each of which is equally likely:

Coin drawn	Side shown	Other side
Double-headed coin	H	H
Double-headed coin	H (the other heads)	H
Ordinary coin	H	T
Ordinary coin	T	H

The last possibility did not occur because the first coin was heads. Therefore, there are three remaining possibilities, each of which is equally likely. Of the three, two of the possibilities will show heads on the other side; only one will show tails on the other side. So the probability that the other side of the coin is heads is two thirds.

p13

99 99/99

p14

6.2832 yards.

The circumference of a circle is 2πr, where r is the radius of the circle. If you want a rope that is one yard above the ground, this new radius R is larger by one yard. So R = r + 1. Let x be the amount of extra rope required. So:

x = (2π(r + 1)) - (2πr)

x = (2πr) + (2π) - (2πr)

x = 2π

π is 3.14159 so x is about 6.2832 yards!

p15

A) 5 (range is the difference between largest and smallest score)

B) 7 (median is the middle value when they are in order of size)

C) 6 (mean is sum of all scores divided by the number of scores)

p16

BAC = 28.1°; Tan BAC = opposite / adjacent = 8/15 = 0.5333; Tan-1 of 0.5333 = 28.1°.

SOHCAHTOA: a way of remembering

SOH stands for Sine equals Opposite over Hypotenuse.

CAH stands for Cosine equals Adjacent over Hypotenuse.

TOA stands for Tangent equals Opposite over Adjacent.

A prime factor tree breaks a number down into its prime number factors

The highest common factor is the biggest number that will go into both 112 and 70. The ones in common for both trees are 2 and 7, and thus the highest common factor is 2 x 7 = 14.

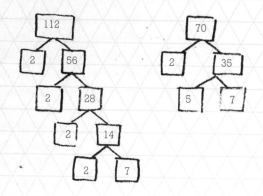

To work out the number of degrees for one item, divide 140 by 35 = 4

Surfboard	Frequency	Angle in pie chart
Longboard	35	140
Shortboard	30	120
Fishboards	11	44
Hybrids	14	56

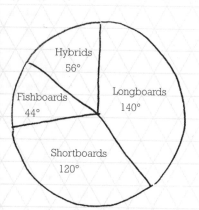

Cost per ounce = cost in cents / weight in ounces
Small bag = 110/ 6 = 18.3
Large bag = 398/ 21 = 18.95
Therefore, it is cheaper to buy small bags of these peanuts!

Double brackets mean four multiplications:
$y \times y = y^2$
$y \times +3 = 3y$
$y \times +7 = 7y$
$+7 \times +3 = 21$
add these together giving $y^2 + 10y + 21$.

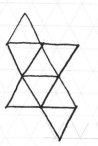

A)

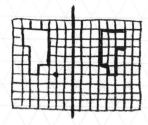

B)

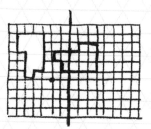

$2.

p24

A)

x	-3	-2	-1	0	1	2	3	4
y	-8	-5	-2	1	4	7	10	13

B)

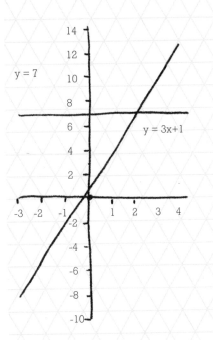

y = 7

y = 3x+1

p25

Approximately 24 yards 11 inches (actual size is 3.5 inches x 250 = 875 inches; one yard is 36 inches, so 875/36 = 24.305)

p26

A) If shortest side is x units, then:
each longest side is x + 2 units
each middle length side is x +1 units;
the cuboid has two faces each of short x medium, medium x long and long x short, or
$2 x(x +1) + 2(x +1)(x + 2) + 2 x(x + 2)$
B) when $2 x(x +1) + 2(x +1)(x + 2) + 2 x(x + 2) = 52$, work out x.
Simplifying the equation gives $6x^2 + 7x + 2 = 52$
x = 2 units.

p27

a) Angles in a triangle add up to 180°,
so x = 180 – 30 – 35 = 115°.
b) The missing angle of the quadrilateral (next to x) is 180 – 115 = 65°
There are two y angles and all angles in a quadrilateral add up to 360°, so 2y = 360 – 95 – 65 = 200°. Therefore, y = 100°.

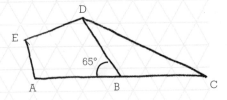

p28

The 3 pounds of nails cost 3 × $1.95 = $5.85.
The cost of the 0.4 pounds of washers is then $6.93 – $5.85 = $1.08.
One pound of washers thus costs 1.08/0.4 = $2.70.

p29

A)

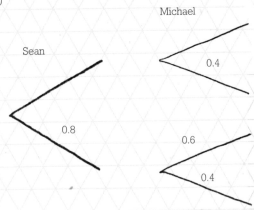

B) 0.2 × 0.6 = 0.12

p30

The volume of the tank is cross-section multiplied by length:[(1.5 + 3)/2 × 2.25] × 2.5 = 12.66 cubic yards;
85% of 12.66 = 10.76 yard³ and as 1 yard³ = 202 gallons,
the total it could hold is 2,174 gallons. At the flow rate of 150 gallons per minute, it would fill in 2,174/100 = 14.5 minutes.
But as it has already filled for 1 minute, Marie will have to wait 13.5 minutes to fill the tank.

p31

(a) ABC is a scaled up version of NOP, so the ratio, or scale factor, of big side to small side in ABC is the same as that in NOP:

big side/small side = 25/10 = 2.5.
So BC = OP × 2.5 = 8 × 2.5 = 20 inches.

(b) This time the scale factor is reversed to find the smaller length:

NO = AB/2.5 = 15/2.5 = 6 inches.

p32

Ratio required is s/w.
Airplane flying against the wind can be expressed as d = 8(s − w),
and with the wind d = 7(s + w).
Put them together to give:
8(s − w) = 7(S + w)
Solving this gives: s/w = 15.

p33

Area of a trapezoid = ½ h × (base 1 + base 2).
The area of this trapezoid can be expressed as:
270 = ½ h * (10 + 10 + 3 + 4)
This gives h = 20.
To find the perimeter, work out L and R using Pythagoras' theorem:
$L^2 = 20^2 + 3^2$, so L = sqrt(409)
$R^2 = 20^2 + 4^2$, so R = sqrt(416)
perimeter = sqrt(409) + 10 + sqrt(416) + 17 = 27 + sqrt(409) + sqrt(416).

p34

If the selling price of house is x, then 5% x = 13,750.
Then x = 13,750 × $^{100}/_5$ = 275,000.

p35

x + y + z = $150.
If x = cost of one shirt, y = cost of one pair of trousers and z = cost of one hat, then
4x + 4y + 2z = 560 and 9x + 9y + 6z = 1,290.
Solve for x + y by dividing the terms in the second equation by 3, giving 3x + 3y + 2z = 430, and then taking this from the first equation, giving: x + y = 130.
Then putting this in the second equation gives
3(130) + 2z = 430, making z = 20.
So x + y + z = 130 + 20.

p36

Height of first, faster burning candle, H1 = (1−T/4), where T is time of burning
Height of second candle, H2 = (1−T/5) .
We want the point when 2 × H1 = H2, so:
2 (1−T/4) = 1−T/5, which reduces to 1 = T/2 − T/5, or 10 = 3T, so T =10/3 hours, or 3 h 20 minutes.

p37

For compound interest, total amount A after t years is given by: A = P(1 + r)^t, where P is the initial lottery winnings (principal), r is the rate and t is time in years.
1 year: A = 2,000(1 + 0.03)^1 = $2,060
2 years: A = 2,000(1 + 0.03)^2 = $2,121.80
3 years: A = 2,000(1 + 0.03)^3 = $2,185.45.

p38

The speed of Patricia's car is 62.5 mph.
distance = speed × time, and Patricia and Jack travel the same distance, so
2 hours at Patricia's speed = Jack's longer journey (2 hours plus 0.5 hours) at 50mph, so Patricia's speed = (2.5 × 50)/2.

p39

3,000 revolutions / minute = 3,000 × 360 degrees in 60 seconds
Number of degrees in a second = (3,000 × 360)/60 = 18,000.

p40

The whole cheese can be cut into 10 wedges with 360−350 = 10 degrees left over.
Each degree of cheese weighs 900 g/ 360° = 2.5 g and therefore the left over cheese weighs 25g.

p41

The total flag area is 13 stripes of which the white stripe area is:
3 × whole stripes + 3 × 60% stripes = 4.8 stripes, so the fraction of white stripes is 4.8/12 or 40%.

p42

216 (17+1) × 12.

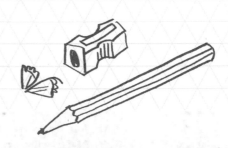

p43

The numbers at each corner indicate clients who use just
1 ISP: 7 + 9 + 8 +8 = 32 clients, so the proportion using
2 or more ISPs is 80 – 32 = 48/80 = 60%.
Therefore, the total expected to use 2 or more ISPs in a
population of 10,000 is 6,000.

p44

The first set has three options and the rest have two options to
avoid neighboring lights being the same:
3 × 2× 2× 2× 2× 2× 2× 2 = 384.

p45

If the three pomegranates are P1, P2 and P3, then
P1 + P2 = 400g
P1 + P3 = 424g
P2 + P3 = 448g
The lightest pomegranate must be P1 as it is in the two lightest
pairs of fruit. To find P1, add the first two expressions: 2P1
+P2 +P3 = 824 and take away the third to remove P2 and P3,
giving 2P1 = 376, so the lightest pomegranate weighs 188g.

p46

If the initial bearing is 28°, its adjacent angle is 90 -28 = 62°,
so the supplementary angle at the change of bearing is 180 –
62 = 118°. The distance of the island from port, r, can then be
calculated using this angle and the law of cosines:
$r^2 = (7.5)^2 + (4.1)^2 – 2(7.5)(4.1) \cos 118° = 101.93$ and
therefore r = 10.1 miles.

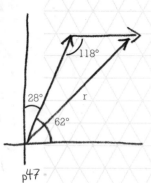

p47

Total number of socks is 12; the probability of white then white
or black then black is:
(7/12 × 6/11) + (5/12 × 4/11) = 42/132 + 20/132 = 62/132 or
31/66.

p48

The answer is approximately 46 feet.
Six dimensions are given but there are actually 7 strips on
the water feature plan and the width of the water at the very
bottom is 0 feet. Thus:
(0 + 56 + 64 + 56 + 44 + 46 + 54)/7 = 320/7 = 46.

p49

The woman drinks one shot per day for 30 days. At the same
rate, she drinks 18 in 18 days, so her daughter drinks 30–18 =
12. The daughter drinks 12 in 18 days, so will drink 30 in 30 ×
18/12 = 30 × 3/2 = 45 days.

p50

X = (678 – 56)/2 = 311
Y = 311 + 56 = 367

p51

Outward journey: 2.25 + (7 × .75) = $7.50
Return journey: 4.00 + (7 × .75) = $9.25
Total: $16.75

p52

Sum as: 30 + 28 + 26… 4 + 2, or
30 × 15 –2(1+2 +3…14) = 450 –(2 × 105) = 240 minutes = 4
hours.

p53

$99 × 10^6$
$0.99 × 10^8$
$990,000 × 10^2$
These are all 99,000,000.

p54

The mouse burns ten times as much energy as the elephant
per ounce per day.
The elephant weighs 12,000 × 16 oz = 192,000 oz giving a per
oz calorie consumption of 40,000/192,000 = 0.2.
The mouse consumes 2 calories per oz.

p55

The gain in height of water is h, the volume of water pushed up
is the volume of the sphere, and the sphere radius r is 6/2 = 3
inches; so $9 × 9 × h = 4/3 \, πr^3$
Solving for $h = 4/(81 × 3) \, π \, 3^3 = 4 × 3× 3× 3/81× 3 \, π =$
$4/9 \, π$ inches

p56

You use three or four numbers to sum to 100:
49 + 41 + 10 = 100
49 + 32 + 19 = 100
45 + 24 + 19 + 12 = 100.

p57

Her start work time is 09:15.
If T is the time from 08.14 to start work time, then:
$48 \times (T - 1)/60 = 45 \times (T + 3)/60$
$48T - 48 = 45T + 135$, so T = 61 minutes, and therefore
the start of work time is 08:14 + 61 = 09:15.

p58

Rotate the triangle 90° around its left-hand vertex and shift
down by 2.

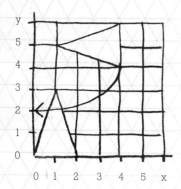

p59

The circumference and therefore the spinning speed is
proportional to its diameter, so the right-hand gear spins at:
$100 \times (8/7) \times (8/7) \times (8/7) = 100 \times 512/343 = $ about 149 rpm.

p60

(A) (1,2) (which is below the line)

p61

On Monday, Tim picked X zucchini, so
$X + (X+6) + (X+12) + (X+18) + (X+24) = 5X + 60 = 100$
Giving X = 8, so on Wednesday, he picked 8 + 12 = 20
zucchini, enough to bake 10 cakes.

p62

270°.
The house apex diagram is a pentagon. Connecting each
vertex to the centre gives five triangles and the sum of angles
of each triangle is 180°.
The sum of the five angles at center of the pentagon is 360°,
so the sum of all angles in the pentagon is:

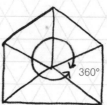

$5 \times 180° - 360° = 540°$
Thus the sum of angles B and D is 540 – (3×90) = 270°.

p63

Every other number is odd, so sum of first 200 is 1 + 3 +5 +…
399 =
(1 + 399) × 100/2 = 20,000.

p64

Probability of a four wins in a row is:
$5/8 \times 5/8 \times 5/8 \times 5/8 = 125/4{,}096 = 0.03$ or 3%.

p65

210.
Number of combinations of 4 out of 10, is:
$10! / (4! \times (10–4)!) = 7 \times 8 \times 9 \times 10/ 4 \times 3 \times 2 \times 1 = 210$.

p66

X is the order on a table, and the student requires that X
(17/100) = $6, and thus
X = 600/17 = $35.3 or approximately $35 per table spent.

p67

60°; it is an equilateral triangle with each interior angle the
same.

p68

1888, which is MDCCCLXXXVIII.

p69

Years until 2100 is 2100 – 2018 = 82
82 = (6 × 12) + 10 and the tenth animal after the Dog is the
Monkey.

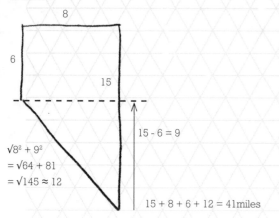

p70

41 miles .

$\sqrt{8^2 + 9^2}$
$= \sqrt{64 + 81}$
$= \sqrt{145} \approx 12$

15 - 6 = 9

15 + 8 + 6 + 12 = 41 miles

p71

Assuming one man marries one woman, 75% is the same as ¾ and 80% is the same as 4/5, so
¾M = 4/5W or 15M = 16W, so M:W = 16/15.

p72

Probability of green in Bag 1 is 3/8 and then from Bag 2 1/5, giving probability of two greens of 3/40.

p73

If winner gets X% votes, the runner-up gets X/3% , so:
X + X/3 + 10 = 100%
4/3X = 90, so X = 67.5%.

p74

Base is 5 billiard ball diameters, so increasing by 40% gives a length (n) of seven diameters, so:
n (n + 1)/2 = 7 (8)/2 = 28 balls.

p75

The cost of one mp3 download is $15.36/6 = $2.56.
Jane's five mp3 downloads, therefore, cost 5 × 2.56 = $12.80, so her two CDs cost spent $27.68 − 12.80 = 14.88, and thus one CD costs $7.44.

p76

A) 8p + 14
B) If p2 = 8p + 14, this gives quadratic equation p² − 87 − 14 = 0, giving the terms for the quadratic formula: a = 1, b = −8, c = −14:

$$x = \frac{--8 \pm \sqrt{-8^2 - 4x - 14}}{2} \quad \text{or} \quad x = \frac{8 \pm \sqrt{-120}}{2}$$

giving p = 9.5

p77

65 is incorrect; it should be 67.

p78

If T is the total in the survey and the difference between NO and YES is 93, then 93 = (7/8 − 1/8)T = 6/8 or ¾T ; therefore, T = 124.

p79

A) n²
B) n² + 2
C) n³/2

p80

A) 135π square inches
Area of a circle = πr² , radius of the clock is 18 inches, and fraction of the clock between the hands is 5/12, so:
area = π × 18² × 5/12 = 135π.
B) Circumference of a circle = πd and fraction of the clock between the hands is 5/12, so:
arc length = π × 36 × 5/12 = 15π.

p81

7,674,418,190.
Expected population rise in 2018 is 1.09% of approximately 7,632,819,325 , or 83,197,731. The remainder of 2018 is 6 months or ½ a year, so the likely increase in population is 41,598,865, giving a total of 7,674,418,190.

p82

Car A and B each pay $3.

p83

160 cubic inches.
Scaling factor is ratio of given areas = 32:72 = 4:9, and thus scaling factor of lengths is √4: √9 = 2:3 and of volumes is 2³:3³ = 8:27.
Volume J = 8/27 × 540 = 160 cubic inches.

p84

Ratio of parts is 1 : ¼ : 3¾, which is simplified to 4:1:15, giving a total of 20 parts. The weight of dry materials is 85% of 20 pounds OR 17 pounds.

This means that one part weighs 17/20 = 0.85 pounds, which means that Aziz must use:

4	3.4 pounds cement
1	0.85 pounds lime
15	12.75 pounds sand.

p85

Car A speed: 2.5 miles in 1 minute (= 150 mph)
Car B speed: 2.5 miles in 1.25 minutes (= 120 mph)
Car A hits the start line every minute, but car B coincides with car A on completing its 4th lap--after 5 minutes. By then car A has completed 5 laps.
In the 5 minutes, car A will have traveled 5 × 2.5 or 12.5 miles, whereas car B will have traveled 4 x 2.5 or 10 miles.

p86

Time (t hours)	Cumulative frequency
0≤t<4	5
0≤t<8	32
0≤t<12	69
0≤t<16	93
0≤t<20	100

From the resulting graph, drawing a vertical from 13 hours to the frequency curve and then a horizontal line to the number of students gives the cumulative frequency of 80. The number of students doing 11 or more hours homework is the area above the line, representing 100–80 = 20 students.

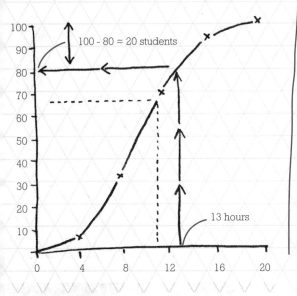

p87

Annette scored highest, because 43 > 42
(which is 56% of 75) > 40 (8/15 of 75)

p88

42°.
Internal angles of triangle = 180° = 7x + 53 + 18 + 90, which makes x = 6
7(6) = 42° and 5(6) + 18 = 48°.

p89

Average speed is actually less than this: 37.5mph.
First part of trip: 50mph × 3 hours = 150 miles
Second part of trip: 150 miles/ 30mph = 5 hours; so total distance = 300 miles, total time = 8 hours, and average speed 300/8 = 37.5.

p90

Statement	Equation	Graph
1	$y = kx$	D
2	$y = k/x$	A
3	$y = kx^2$	B
4	$y = k/x^2$	C

p91

79 years × 365 days × 24 hours × 60 minutes × 80 beats = 3,321,792,000 or around 3 billion beats. (Actually it will be much more than this as your heart beats faster as an infant and when doing any exercise.)

p92

$1/5$.
At the start, pail 1 = 5 gallons water or 5W, and pail 2 = 5 gallons vinegar or 5V;
transferring 1W from pail 1 to pail 2 gives:
pail 1 = 4W and pail 2 = 5V + 1W
transferring a gallon (one sixth of total volume) from pail 2 to pail 1 gives:
pail 1 = 4W + ($1/6$)(5V + 1W) or (4 + $1/6$)W + $5/6$V and pail 2 = $5/6$(5V + 1W); so proportion of vinegar to water in pail 1 is $5/6/ 4^1/6$ = 5/25 = $1/5$.

p93

6 feet.
The square has a perimeter of 16 feet and therefore an area 4 × 4 feet = 16 square feet; the rectangle area is 0.75 × 16 = 12 square feet; if its width is 2 feet, then its length is 6 feet.

Area of a circle 40 square miles $=\pi r^2 \approx 3.1416\, r2$, so r $=\sqrt{(40/3.1416)} = 3.6$ miles, Maximum length across a circle is its diameter = 7.2 miles. Therefore, the most the taxi can charge is $8 \times 4 = \$32$.

159,600.
Each of the four people send 3 emails; so if N is the number of people, then number of emails is $N \times N{-}1$; therefore, $400 \times (400{-}1) = 159{,}600$.

6 fish.
The volume of the top inch of the aquarium is 500 cubic inches. Adding the castle to the aquarium increases the volume by $400/500 = 4/5$ inches. The remaining volume before the water overflows is 1/5 inch $\times 500 = 100$ cubic inches. Therefore, no more than $100/15 = 6$ fish can be added before the water overflows.

6.
The half bangle between 11 and 29 has $29{-}11 = 18$ beads, so the total on the bangle is $2 \times 18 = 36$.

1.88 pounds.
The weight of the slice without water is $1{-}0.92 \times 5 = 0.4$ pounds.
The new weight of the slice after being in the sun is $0.4/(1{-}0.78)$ or $0.4/0.22$.

Opposite angles are equal, so $5x - 20 = 2x + 43$ and therefore $x = 21°$
Co-interior angles sum to $180°$, so $(2x + 43) + (4y - 5x) = 180°$; using $x = 21$ and solving for y gives $4y - 20 = 180$ and thus $y = 50°$.

A) 0 yards/s²
B) −4 yards/s²
C) 40 yards

Five pieces requires 4 cuts, so the remaining percentage of the original volume is $100 - (4 \times 2.5) = 90\%$ divided into 5 pieces makes each piece approximately 18%.

Four.

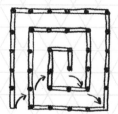

67.
If one month is not counted (1/12) each year and 2 days out of 7 days are not counted , the 44 years represents $(11/12) \times (5/7)$ of his actual age; thus
Actual age = $44 \times 7 \times 12/(5 \times 11) = 28 \times 12/5 = 67.2$ years.

Number of male shareholders is 50.
$(male/5 \times 1{,}000) + (female/4 \times 1{,}000) = 30{,}000$ which can be rewritten as:
male/5 + female/4 = 30 or 4 male + 5 female = 600;
substituting male = 130 − female gives:
4 male + 5(130 − male) = 600, so male = 650 − 600 = 50.

29, which is the product of the largest numbers minus the square of the smallest.

Filling in a Venn diagram with given and computed values gives:

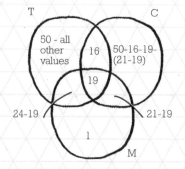

OR ;

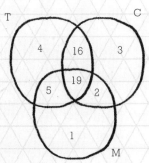

so

A) 44/50 (all values in tea circle out of total in survey)

B) 21/44 (sum of T+C and T+M out of the 44 tea drinkers)

p107

An accurate watch would have completed 9 hours between 6 am (06:00:00) and 3 pm (15:00:00), but this watch loses 9 × 12 = 108 seconds or 1 minute 48 seconds. So the time shown should be 14:58:12.

p108

200 apples.

Increased by 100% has the same meaning as doubled, and number of years is 6 − 1 = 5

(Number of apples) × 2^5 = 6,400 and therefore, number of apples = 6,400/32 = 200.

p109

If D is the number of days, then:

12 × 8 = (12 + 4) × D; therefore, D = 96/16 = 6 days.

p110

120 gallons.

Square area is sum of sides and tops. From each side there are 6 +5 +4 +3 +2 +1 = 21 squares, giving a total of 84 squares. From the top, some squares are covered by those on top, but the total area is 6 × 6 = 36 squares; total squares is 84 + 36 = 120 squares needing 120 gallons of paint.

p111

120.

The six lengths is the same as ¼ + 1/5 = 1/20. Therefore, the total distance intended is 20 × 6 = 120 lengths.

p112

120°.

Angle PQR is 90° and sum of internal angle in a triangle is 180°; therefore, QPR + QRP = 180 − 90 = 90°

The sum of angles in a quadrilateral is 360°. In RSTU, we know that RST is 90°. The RUT internal angle is 120° so the external angle in the quadrilateral is 240°. This means that SRU + SUT = 360 − 240 − 90 = 30°. Therefore, the sum of the angles required in this problem is 30 + 90 = 120°.

p113

Draw a pyramid on each side of the magic square and then fill in numbers sequentially in the diagonals. Then relocate these numbers in the opposite hole in the square!

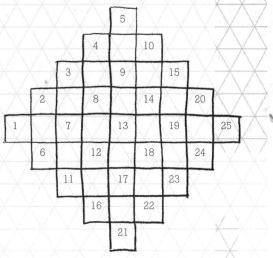

3	16	9	22	15
20	8	21	14	2
7	25	13	1	19
24	12	5	18	6
11	4	17	10	23

p114

$3,740.

Sales × 7.5/100 = 280.50 which gives sales = 28,050/7.5.

p115

275 years.

You have 2 parents, 2^2 grandparents, 2^3 great grandparents, and so on up to 2^n ancestors. Closest n value is 11, because 2^{11} = 2,048. With 25 years per generation, the answer is 25 × 11.

p116

100 miles.

Total distance is distance downhill x and distance uphill y, and time = distance/speed; so the first journey is expressed as x/50 + y/20 = 2 and the return leg as x/20 + y/50 = 5. Solving each and summing gives: 2x + 5y = 200 and 5x + 2y = 500, so x + y = 100.

p117

3

4^3 − 56 = 8!

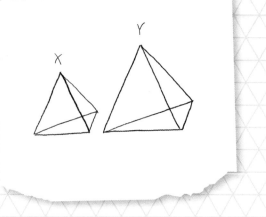

ISBN: 978-0-9574232-4-4

This book was conceived, designed and produced by Paperwasp,
an imprint of Balley Design Limited.
The Loft, 45 Grantham Road,
Brighton, East Sussex, BN1 6EF
United Kingdom

Creative Director: Simon Balley
Designer: Kevin Knight
Project editor: Richard Spilsbury

Visit our website
www.paperwaspbooks.com

Printed and bound in China

10 9 8 7 6 5 4 3 2 1